114

First Fairy Tales

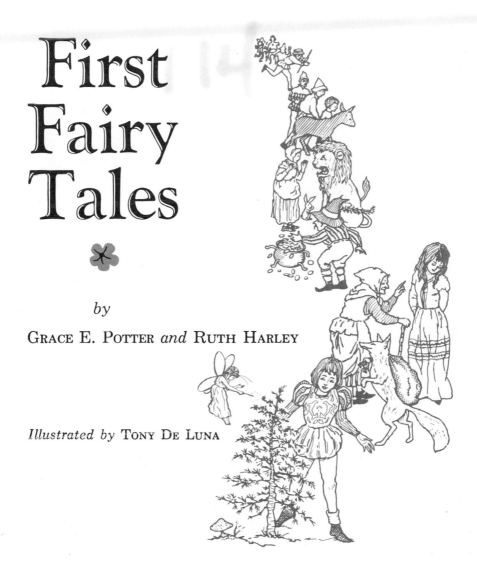

by

GRACE E. POTTER *and* RUTH HARLEY

Illustrated by TONY DE LUNA

CHARLES E. MERRILL BOOKS, INC.

Columbus 16, Ohio

TABLE OF CONTENTS

LIBRARY OF CONGRESS CATALOG CARD NUMBER: 64-13114

The Little Pine Tree

Once there was a little tree.
It was a pine tree.
The little pine tree did not have
leaves like other trees.
It had dark green needles.

Its green needles smelled good.
When the wind blew, they made
a sweet kind of music.

But the little tree was not happy.
"I wish I had leaves of gold,"
it said one day.

The Tree Fairy heard this.
She blew softly on the tree.
At once the green needles turned
into leaves of gold.

But that night a bad man came.
He pulled off the golden leaves.
Then the little pine tree had
no leaves at all!

"Oh, dear!" said the little tree.
"Bad men take golden leaves!
I wish I had leaves of glass!"
So the Tree Fairy tied leaves
of glass on the little pine tree.

But then the wind started to blow.
It soon broke all the glass leaves.
They fell to the ground in pieces.
Again the little tree had no leaves!

"Oh, dear!" said the little tree.
"Bad men take golden leaves.
The wind breaks glass leaves.
I wish I had pretty green leaves!"

Again the Tree Fairy heard this.
She shook green leaves over the tree.

Soon a goat came along.
It ate all the leaves off the tree.

"Oh, dear!" cried the little tree.
"Bad men take golden leaves.
The wind breaks glass leaves.
Goats eat green leaves.
I wish I had my needles again!"

The Fairy gave the tree its wish.
Never again did it wish for anything
that a pine tree should not have!

The Two Frogs

Two little frogs lived in Japan.
One frog lived in the city of Osaka.
The other lived in the city of Kioto.
Between these two cities was
a big hill.

One day the Osaka frog said,
"I have never been away from home.
I am going to Kioto to see the world."
He said good-by to his family
and started on his way.

The Kioto frog said,
"I have never been away from home.
I am going to Osaka to see the world."
He said good-by to his family
and started on his way.

The two frogs met on a high hill.
The road was not at all wide.
They could not get by each other.
"Let us stand up on our back legs.
Then we can each see the world,"
the frogs said.

So the two frogs stood as high as
they could on their back legs.
Each one tried hard to see
whatever was in front of him.

But then their eyes were in the back
of their heads, not the front!
So the two frogs did not see
where they were going!
They only saw where they had been!

"Why, Osaka is just like Kioto!"
said the frog from Kioto.

"Why, Kioto is just like Osaka!"
said the frog from Osaka.

"All places are just alike,"
said the two silly frogs.
"Why should we go far away to see
the same old things?
Let us go home."

And they did.

The Golden Eggs

There was once a poor farmer.
All he had was a white goose.
But one fine day he found an egg
made of gold in the goose's nest.
The next day the farmer found
another golden egg in the nest!

"What a fine goose!" he said.
"I can sell these golden eggs!"

Every morning the farmer found
a fine golden egg in the nest.
Every day he sold the golden egg.
Little by little he was getting rich.

But the farmer was in a hurry.
He wanted to be rich right away.
   One day he said to himself,
"My goose lays only one egg a day.
But perhaps she has many more
golden eggs inside her!"
   He couldn't stop thinking about it.
At last he said one morning,
"I shall look and see!"
   So the farmer killed the poor goose.

But when he looked inside the bird,
there was no gold there at all!
The inside of the goose looked just
like the inside of any other goose.

"Dear, oh, dear!" said the farmer.
"Why was I in such a hurry?
Now I shall be poor again!
I have killed the goose that laid
the golden eggs!"

Numskull and the Rabbit

Numskull was a very big, bad lion.
The other animals were afraid of him.
He was much stronger than they were.
Every day he killed many of them
and ate them for his dinner.

At last the animals made a plan.
"Numskull, listen to us," they said.

"Every day we shall send you
a different animal for your dinner.
If we do this, will you stop hurting
the rest of us?"

"Well, I'll try it," said Numskull.

So every day a different kind
of animal was sent to the lion.
At last came the rabbit's turn.
He went, but he moved very slowly.
He was in no hurry to get there.

On the way he said to himself,
"I am just a small rabbit, but maybe
I can trick Numskull."

When he got there, Numskull roared,
"You are late—where have you been?
Besides, you are too small!
I am very, very hungry!"
The rabbit said, "Don't be cross.
The animals knew I was too small,
so they sent five other rabbits, too."
"Where are they?" roared Numskull.

"They started out," said the rabbit.
"But on the way we met another lion.
He kept the five other rabbits."

"Kept my rabbits?" roared Numskull.

"Yes, he did," said the rabbit.
"He said he was stronger than you.
If you didn't believe it, you could try
to get the rabbits back from him."

"Take me to him!" roared Numskull.
"I'll show him who is stronger!"

The rabbit took Numskull to a well.
"There he is, down there," he said.

Numskull looked down into the well.
He saw himself in the deep water.
But he thought that he was seeing
another lion.

Numskull roared down into the well.
The echo sounded as if another lion
were roaring back at him.

At last Numskull jumped down
into the well to kill the other lion.
Down, down, down he went,
and he never came back.

That was the end of Numskull.
(It was the end of the other lion, too!)
The little rabbit ran home to tell
the good news to all his friends.

A Hard Lesson

One morning a father and his son
were taking their donkey to town.
They were going to sell the donkey.

Along the way they met some boys.
The boys laughed at them.
"Why do you walk?" they asked.
"One of you could be riding
on the donkey's back!"

"You are right," said the man.
"I had not thought of that!"
So he put his son on the donkey.
They went on their way.

Next they met an old man.
"What a bad boy!" cried the old man.
"How can you ride the donkey
while your poor father walks?"

"I am sorry, Father!" said the boy.

He jumped off the donkey at once,
and his father climbed on.

Soon they met a young woman.
The woman said, "Of all things!
A big strong man rides and makes
his little son walk!"

"Oh, dear!" cried the father.
"You had better get up here, too!"
So the boy got up behind him.

Another woman saw them and cried,
"Oh, that poor, poor donkey!
He has to carry the two of you!
It would be better if you were
to carry the donkey!"
Now the father and his son wanted
very much to do the right thing.
They climbed down off the donkey.
Then they tied its legs together
over a long, strong stick.
The father took one end of the stick.

His son took the other end of it.
In that way they went down the road,
carrying the donkey between them.

At last the father, his son, and
the donkey came to a river near town.
They looked so funny that everyone
came running to laugh at them!

The noise made the donkey afraid.
He jumped and kicked his legs around.
The father and the son couldn't hold
onto the stick any longer.

The donkey fell into the river
and was never seen again!

Soon the father and his son
started sadly on the way home.
After a while the father said,
"Well, my son, we lost the donkey,
but we learned one good lesson—
When you try to please everyone,
you end up by pleasing no one!"

The Cook and the Goose

There was once a very rich man
who had a very poor man for a cook.
One day the rich man did not like
what the poor man was cooking.
He told him to go catch a goose
and cook it.

The poor man caught the goose.
He cooked it over the fire
till it was all brown and soft.

But when he took it from the fire,
he burned his fingers.
He put them into his mouth to cool
them off.

Now a little bit of the goose was
on the poor man's fingers.
"My, that tastes good!" he said.

It made him so hungry that he broke
off a leg of the goose and ate it.
Then he put the goose on the table.

When the rich man saw the goose,
he was not at all happy.
He called the poor man to him.

"Why has this goose only one leg?"
he asked in a loud voice.
"Where is the other leg?"

"Why, goodness!" said the poor man.

"That goose had only one leg when I caught it!"

"Are you sure?" asked the rich man. "I have never heard of a goose with only one leg."

"Come with me," said the poor man. "All the geese have only one leg. I will show you."

The rich man ate the goose first. Then he went with the poor man.

They went down to the river,
where the geese lived.

It was a very cold day.
The geese were not in the water.
They were all standing on the shore.
They were trying to keep warm.
Each of them stood on one leg.

The poor man was pleased.
"See for yourself," he said.
"Each goose has only one leg."

The rich man went over to the geese.
"Boo!" he cried.

All the geese put down both feet.
They ran to the water and swam away.

"Well!" said the rich man.
"Now do the geese have only one leg?"

But the poor man only said,
"You should have said 'Boo!'
to the goose that I cooked for you.
Then perhaps it would have had
two legs, too!"

A Princess for a Prince

Once a King said to his son,
"It is time for you to have a wife."
   "Yes, it is," said the Queen.
"And she must be a real Princess."
   "Well, now," said the Prince.
"<u>You</u> say I must have a wife, and
<u>you</u> say she must be a real Princess.
But <u>I</u> say she must be beautiful!"

"Find her, then," said the King.

The Prince looked and looked.
He found many beautiful girls.
But not one was a Princess.
He found many Princesses.
But not one was beautiful.

One night it rained very hard.
The Prince heard a knock at the door.
Standing outside in the rain was
the most beautiful girl he had ever seen.

"I am a Princess," she said.
"May I come in?"

She did not look like a Princess.
Rain ran down her long black hair.
It dripped off her dress.
It ran into the tops of her shoes.

The Queen told the King and Prince,
"I will find out whether this girl is
a real Princess."

She went to the room that was
to be the Princess's room.
She put a teeny tiny pebble
under the hair mattress on the bed.
Then she put nine more hair mattresses
on top of the first mattress.
Then she put ten feather mattresses
on top of those.

She called the Princess to come.
"You may sleep here," she said.

In the morning, the Queen went
at once to the Princess's room.
"How did you sleep?" she asked.
Just then the King hurried in.
"How did you sleep?" he asked.
Next the Prince came running.
"How did you sleep?" he asked.
"I did not shut my eyes all night.
I was lying on something hard!"
said the Princess.

"I am black and blue all over!
What could have been in my bed?"

Then they all knew that she must
really, truly be a Princess!
Only a real Princess would feel
a pebble under ten hair mattresses
and ten feather ones!

Of course the Prince asked her
to be his wife, and they lived
happily ever after.

The Christmas Tree

It was the night before Christmas.
The children were all in bed.
But the Christmas Fairy was not
in bed.

"I must trim the tree," she said.
"I shall put candy canes on it.
I shall put all kinds of toys on it."

Soon the Christmas tree was ready.
The Christmas Fairy called Tom Cat
and Billy Dog to come see it.
She called Mr. and Mrs. Mouse.

"How beautiful it is!" they cried.

Some spiders who were living
in the same house heard about the tree.
"Please let us see it, too,"
they said to the Fairy.

"All right," the Fairy told them.
"But take care not to touch it."
Then the Fairy went to trim the tree
in the house next door.

The spiders ran to see the tree.
"What a fine tree!" they cried.

They forgot what the Fairy
had said to them.
They ran up and down the tree.
They jumped from branch to branch.
They climbed all over the toys.

But when the sun began to rise,
they ran away.

Soon the Christmas Fairy came back.
She wanted to make sure the tree
was just right.

What do you think she saw?
The tree was all covered
with long gray cobwebs!

But the Fairy knew what to do.
She threw open the curtains and cried,
"Help me, Mr. Sun!"
In came the yellow sunshine.

Soon the children woke up.
They ran into the room
where the tree was standing.
"Oh, come! Oh, see!" they cried.
"See the golden Christmas tree!"
They were right.
The sunshine had turned
every cobweb to gold!

The Big Party

There once was a man named Juba.
One day Juba sat down under a tree.
He had worked hard all morning.
He was very tired.
In a little while he fell asleep.

By and by some children came along.
They saw Juba asleep under the tree.

"Juba knows many good stories,"
one of the children said.
"If we wake him up, perhaps he
will tell us one."

"Yes, yes!" cried all the others.
"Wake up, Juba! Wake up!
Tell us a story, please!"

But Juba did not want to wake up.
He wanted to have a nice long sleep.
"Go away," he said to the children.
"Go away and let me sleep!"

The children would not go away.
Juba saw that he would have to play
a trick on them.

After a little while, he said,
"Aren't you all going to the party?
They are giving cake and candy
to everyone who comes!"

"What party?" the children asked.
"We do not know about a party!"

"Well I know about it," said Juba.
"It is on the other side of town.
You had better hurry over there,
or all the goodies will be gone!"

"Let's go!" cried the children.
"Hurry, or the candy will be gone!"
They all ran off to the other side
of town.

"I fooled them," Juba said.
"There is no party at all!
But now I can get some rest."
Before long he was asleep again.

Soon a noise woke Juba up.
He saw a great many other children,
big and small, running by.

"Candy!" they cried. "Free candy!
Come to the party, Juba!"

Juba had to smile to himself.
"What a good trick!" he said.
"There is no party!"
And he soon fell asleep once more.

But he did not sleep very long.
A new noise woke him up.
Juba saw many grown-ups hurrying by.
Some were friends of his.

"Wait! Stop!" cried Juba.
"Where are you going?"

"We've heard about a free party!"
said one man.

"There will be many good things
to eat and many good things to drink!"
said a woman.

"There will be singing and dancing!"
said someone else.

Juba jumped up and cried,
"Wait for me! Wait for me!"
Then he ran after them as fast as
he could.

But when he got to the other side
of town, there was no party at all.
No good things to eat and drink!
No singing and dancing!

"Well, it serves me right,"
said Juba as he went home again.
"I fooled everyone, even myself!"

Dorta's Dipper

Dorta and her mother lived
in a little house near some woods.
One summer night Dorta's mother
was hard at work cleaning the house.
She said, "I am so thirsty, Dorta!"

Dorta said, "Our well is dry.
But I will get some good, cold water
for you from the spring in the woods.
It is dark out, but I am not afraid."

51

She took an old tin dipper
to carry the water home in.
Then she left the house.

The spring was a long way off.
The night was so dark that Dorta
could not see where she was going.
Sometimes she fell down.
Sometimes stones cut her feet.
But at last she found the spring.

She filled her dipper with water
and started for home.

On the way, she met a dog.
He was very tired and thirsty.
"Poor dog," said Dorta,
giving him some of the water.
As she did so, the old tin dipper
began to shine brightly.
In a minute, it had turned into silver!
Soon Dorta met an old man.
"I am very thirsty," he said.

"Then have some water," said Dorta.
The old man took a deep drink.
As he did so, the silver dipper got
brighter and brighter and brighter.
In a minute, it had turned into gold!

Dorta's mother was waiting
at the door for her when she got home.
She took a drink of the cold water.
"Thank you, my good little girl,"
she said.

As she said this, the whole room
grew very, very bright.
They saw that now the dipper
was made of sparkling diamonds!
All at once the beautiful dipper
rose up into the air.

Out the window it flew.
Up, up, up it went.
When they looked for it,
there it was, up in the night sky!
But the diamonds were not diamonds
any more—they were stars!

Then the dipper called to Dorta,
"Now when you go to the spring
at night, I will show you the way!"

That dipper is still up in the sky.
You can see it if you look at night.
Some people say it is the Big Dipper.
But <u>I</u> say it is Dorta's Dipper.

Lambikin and Drummikin

Once there was a little lamb.
His name was Lambikin.

One day Lambikin said,
"I must go up the hill to see
my dear grandmother.
Her name is Grannikin."

On the way Lambikin met a fox.
The fox said, "Lambikin, Lambikin!
I am going to eat you up!"
But Lambikin said,
  "Oh, do not eat me now!
    I am too small to matter!
  But Grannikin's grass is fresh
      and green,
    And soon I shall be fatter!"
So the fox said, "Very well.
I shall eat you on your way home."

Next Lambikin met a wildcat.
The wildcat said, "Lambikin, Lambikin!
I am going to eat you up!"
Lambikin said, as before,
"Oh, do not eat me now!
I am too small to matter!
But Grannikin's grass is fresh
and green,
And soon I shall be fatter!"
So the wildcat said, "Very well!
I shall eat you on your way home."

Soon Lambikin got to Grannikin's.
He stayed there a long time.
Every day he ate fresh green grass.
Every day he grew fatter and fatter.

At last Lambikin said,
"Grannikin, what shall I do?
I must go home, but the wildcat and
the fox are waiting to eat me up."

Grannikin said,
"Here is an empty barrel.
Its name is Drummikin.
Quick—climb into Drummikin.

"Now you can roll home.
The wildcat and the fox
will not be able to eat you up."

Lambikin climbed into the barrel,
and Grannikin gave it a good push.
Down the hill it rolled.

Soon the barrel came to the wildcat.
The wildcat said, "Stop, Drummikin!
Have you seen Lambikin?"

But Lambikin said in a deep voice,
"Lambikin still eats with Grannikin.
There he'll get much fatter yet!"

Next Drummikin came to the fox.
The fox said, "Stop, Drummikin!
Have you seen Lambikin?"

Lambikin said in the same voice,
"Lambikin still eats with Grannikin.
There he'll get much fatter yet!"

But the fox was not fooled.
"I know you, Lambikin!" he said.
"You are in Drummikin!"
He began to run after Drummikin.

Drummikin went faster and faster.
As it rolled over grass it sang,
"Grass-ikin, pass-ikin!"
As it rolled over stones it sang,
"Stone-ikin, bone-ikin!"

The fox ran fast, too,
but he could not catch Drummikin.

So Lambikin rolled safely
all the way home.

The Gertrude Bird

Once there was a woman who lived
all alone in a fine house.
She had a long nose and red hair.
Her name was Gertrude.

One day Gertrude said to herself,
"I have made a good fire in my stove.
I shall bake myself some sweet cakes."

She put many good things in a dish.
Then she stirred them well.
Soon the cakes were ready to be baked.

Gertrude put the cakes in the oven.
They came out all golden brown.
How good they smelled!

A poor old man was going by
as Gertrude set them outside to cool.
He smelled the good smell and asked,
"Please, may I have one?"

"These cakes are too big for you,"
said Gertrude. "They are for me.
But I will make you a smaller one."

So Gertrude made a little cake.
But the little cake grew and grew!
Soon it was a very big cake!

"Oh!" said Gertrude. "This is
too big for me to give away."
So she made a smaller cake.
But the cake grew and grew and grew.
Soon it was a very, very big cake.

"Oh!" said Gertrude. "This one is
much too big to give away."
Then she made a teeny tiny cake.
But the teeny tiny cake grew
and grew and grew and grew.
Soon it was the biggest cake of all!
"Oh, dear!" said Gertrude.
"They are all much too big!
I will not give you any!"
The old man looked sad.
"You should know me," he said.

"I am the Good Fairy of the Fire.
I do not like people who use
my fire only for themselves.
Now you shall see what it is like
not to have my help."

Then the Good Fairy went away.

As Gertrude watched him go,
she began to feel very strange.
She looked down at her arms.
They had turned into wings!

She felt her nose.
It was longer and sharper!
It had turned into a bird's bill!
Her feet had turned into claws!
Her hair had turned into red feathers.
They covered her head and her face!

Her clothes had all turned
into black feathers!
Gertrude was not a woman any more.
She was a redheaded woodpecker!

Gertrude lives in the woods now.
She works hard to get her food.
She pecks on trees with her long bill.
She eats worms and bugs for dinner.
She never has a fire to cook with.
She never has sweet cakes to eat
any more!

Little Red Hen and the Fox

The little red hen lived
in a little red house near a woods.
She worked very hard every day.
But she was always happy.

On the other side of the woods
lived a bad fox and his old mother.
One day the fox said to his mother,
"Today I am going to catch
the little red hen, so we can eat her!"

"Good," said the mother fox.
"I shall make a big fire while you
are gone, and heat some water.
When you come home with the hen,
I shall cook her for our dinner!"

The bad fox took a big bag.
He went through the woods till he
got to the little red hen's house.
He hid in the grass and waited.

Inside the house, the little hen
was making a new dress for herself.

But soon she saw that she needed
more wood to put on the fire.
She went out to get some sticks.
By mistake, she left the door open.

As soon as her back was turned,
the fox ran into the house.
He hid behind the door.

Soon the little red hen came back.
She closed the door behind her.
Then the bad fox jumped out!

"You can't get away now!" he cried.
"I'm going to catch you and cook you
and eat you!"
The poor hen was very scared.
She flew first on this, then on that,
with the fox after her.
At last, she was so tired
she could not fly any longer.
So the fox jumped and caught her.
He put her into his big bag.

But the fox, too, was tired.
On his way home with the hen,
he stopped in the woods to rest.
He sat down under a tree.
Soon he was fast asleep.

Inside the bag, the little red hen
had been thinking very hard.
Now she said to herself,
"My sewing things are in my pocket!
They will help me!"

She took her sharp little scissors
and cut a good hole in the bag.
Then she climbed out.

"Now I must fool him!" she said.
She looked around for some stones
and put them into the bag.
Then she sewed it up again
and ran home as fast as she could.

After a while the fox woke up.
He picked up the bag again.
This time, it seemed very heavy.
"My, what a fat little hen!" he said.
"She will be good to eat!"

He carried the bag home.
"Here is the little red hen!"
he said to his mother.

"Good, good!" said the mother fox.
"Come, put her into this pot
of hot water."

The fox held the bag up high.
He opened it over the pot of water.
Into the pot fell the stones
with a great big splash!

The hot water went all over the fox
and all over his mother.

"Oh! Oh! Oh!" they both cried.
"We are being cooked alive!"

They ran out of the house and
jumped into the river to cool off.
Down the river they went
and never came back any more!

But the little red hen lived
happy ever after.

Three Billy Goats Gruff

Once there were three billy goats.
Their last name was Gruff.
The three goats lived near a river.
On the other side was a grassy hill.

Now a bridge went across the river.
But under the bridge lived a Troll.
The Troll had eyes as big as plates.
His nose was as long as a broomstick.
He liked to eat people up.
    One day the three goats said,
"Let's all go over and eat
that green grass on the other side!"

The smallest billy goat went first.
"Trip-trip, trip-trip, trip-trip,"
went his little feet on the bridge.

"Who's tripping across my bridge?"
called the old Troll.

"It is I, Little Billy Goat Gruff,"
said the smallest goat.

"I am going to eat you up!"
cried the Troll.

"Oh, please do not eat me up,"
said the smallest goat.

"My brother will be here soon.
He is bigger than I am.
He will be better to eat!"

"Well, I will wait," said the Troll.
"But hurry and get off my bridge!"

So Little Billy Goat Gruff ran
up the hill to eat the green grass.

Next came the second billy goat.
"Trip-trap, trip-trap, trip-trap,"
went his feet on the bridge.

"Who's trip-trapping on my bridge?"
called the old Troll.

"It is I, Middle Billy Goat Gruff,"
said the second billy goat.

"I am going to eat you up!"
cried the Troll.

"Oh, please do not eat me up,"
said the second billy goat.
"My brother will be here soon.
He is bigger than I am.
He will be best to eat!"

"Well, I will wait," said the Troll,
just as he had before.
"But hurry and get off my bridge!"

So Middle Billy Goat Gruff ran
up the hill to eat the green grass.

Soon the big billy goat came along.
"Trap-trap, trap-trap, trap-trap!"
went his big feet on the bridge.

"Who is trap-trapping on my bridge?"
called the old Troll.

"It is I, Big Billy Goat Gruff,"
said the big billy goat.

"I have been waiting for you!"
cried the Troll.
"I am going to eat you up!"

But Big Billy Goat Gruff said,
"Well, come along!
Come right this way!
I'll show you how
I like to play!
I'll hit you once,
And down you'll go—
Into the river, far below!"
Then the big billy goat ran
at the Troll as fast as he could!
He hit him with his strong horns!

He threw him into the river!
Down, down, down went the Troll.
   Then Big Billy Goat Gruff crossed
the bridge and ran up the hill.
All three goats ate the green grass.

Snip, snap, snout!
This tale's told out!
If you look, you'll see them still—
Three fat goats on a high green hill!

The Golden Touch

King Midas was a very rich man.
He had bags and bags of gold.
But in spite of all the gold
he had, the King was not happy.
He wanted still more gold.

One night when he was counting
his money, he said out loud,
"How I wish that everything I touch
would turn into gold!"

To his surprise, a voice said,
"I will give you your wish."

King Midas stared in surprise.
There on the table was a little man
he had never seen before.

"What do you mean?" asked the King.

"It will start in the morning,"
the little man said.
"When you get up, everything
you touch will turn into gold."

The King was very happy.
He could hardly sleep all night.
He kept thinking of all the gold
he would have in the morning.

The next day, he jumped out of bed.
He ran and put his hand on a table.
It turned into shining gold!
He ran around the room.
Everything he touched turned into gold!
Even his clothes turned into gold
when he put them on!

He ran out into the garden.
He touched the roses there.
At once they turned hard and golden.
So did the leaves and the trees
and even the grass.

"How beautiful!" cried the King.
"How rich I am! Gold! Gold! Gold!"

At last he grew hungry.
He went to have his breakfast.

His knife and fork turned into gold
when he picked them up!
The dishes turned into gold!
Even the food turned into gold!

But when he saw the golden food,
the King grew a little afraid.
"What shall I do?" he cried.
"I cannot eat gold eggs
or drink gold milk!"

Just then his little girl ran
into the room looking for him.

"Oh, Father!" she cried.
"What has happened to my garden?
All the flowers are hard and ugly!"

Before King Midas could stop her,
the little girl ran to him.
She threw her arms around him.
At once she was turned into gold!

"What have I done?" cried the King.
"Why did I want so much gold?
Now even my dear little girl
has turned into gold!"

All at once a voice asked,
"Are you not happy, King Midas?"
It was the little man who had given
the King his wish.

"No, no, no, I am not happy at all!"
cried the poor King.

"I never want to see gold again!
All I want is my little girl!"

"Then go and jump into the river,"
the little man said.
"The river will wash every bit
of the golden touch off of you.
Fill this pot with the water, too.
The water will change everything
back to what it was before."

The King jumped into the river.
His clothes were no longer gold!

Then he ran back and sprinkled some
of the water on his little girl.
At once she came to life again.

They both went into the garden.
They sprinkled the water everywhere.
The trees and grass turned green!
The roses were all red and white!

Then King Midas knew
what it was like to be really happy.
He gave all his money to the poor.
He never again wished to have
the golden touch.

Aiken Drum

Once there was a little town
that was near a big woods.
Many people lived in the town.
They were poor and had to work hard.
All day they worked in the fields.
They came back to their homes
only at night.

One day a strange little man came
out of the woods.
He was no bigger than a bird.
He had pointed toes and pointed ears.
He was dressed all in brown.

"Who are you?" the people asked
the little man.

"I am a brownie," he said.
"My name is Aiken Drum.
I see you working every day.
Please let me help you."

One of the men said,
"How much pay do you want?"
But when he looked, Aiken Drum
was gone!
"Where did he go?" everyone asked.
"Why did he go away?"

Only Granny knew. She said,
"Brownies don't work for money.
They never work for pay.
They work just for the love of it,
All the whole long day!"

The people called and called.
But Aiken Drum did not come back.
Soon they stopped talking about him.
They did not think of him again.

Then one year the people
in the town had more work to do
than ever before.
They worked all day.
They worked all night.

One day all the men and women
went to work in the fields.
But when they got there,
they could not believe their eyes.
"Look!" they cried. "The corn is cut!
The gardens are watered!
The fields are plowed!"

That night when they got home
the cows had been milked.
The pigs had been fed.
The houses had been cleaned.

"Who has done it?" they asked.

"We know," said the children.
"It was Aiken Drum! We saw him!
As he was going home, he stopped
to dance with us!"

Every day Aiken Drum came to help.
Every day he stopped to dance
with the children.

Every night the people set out
a bowl of milk for Aiken Drum.
Every morning it was gone.
But no one saw Aiken Drum
except the children.

One night the children said,
"Aiken Drum needs new clothes!"
Then all the mothers cried,
"Yes! He must be tired of brown!
Let us make him a gay new suit!"

So they made a dark blue cap,
a red coat, and bright green pants.
They even made some yellow shoes.
Then they put all the clothes
beside the bowl of milk.

The next day the hat and coat
and pants and shoes were still there!
The bowl of milk was there, too!

Aiken Drum never came again
to help the people with their work.
He never came again to dance
with the children.

Everyone asked, "Where is Aiken?
Why did he go away?"

Granny said, "You hurt his feelings.
I told you before—

Brownies don't work for money.
They never work for pay.
They work just for the love of it,
All the whole long day!"

The Gingerbread Boy

One day an old woman was making
gingerbread for her dinner.
She cut out a Gingerbread Boy
and put him into the oven to bake.

Soon the Gingerbread Boy was done.
When the old woman opened
the oven door, out he jumped.

"My, how good you smell," she said.
"I think I'll eat you right now."

But the Gingerbread Boy said,
"You'll have to catch me first!"
And he ran out of the house
and down the road.

The old woman ran after him,
but she could not catch him.

Soon the Gingerbread Boy came
to a field with a horse in it.

"How good you smell," the horse said.
"I think I'll eat you right now!"

But the Gingerbread Boy said,
"You'll have to catch me first!
The old woman cannot catch me.
And YOU cannot catch me, either!"

The horse jumped over the wall
and ran after the Gingerbread Boy.
But he could not catch him.

Next the Gingerbread Boy came
to a woods where a big bear lived.
"How good you smell!" said the bear.
"I think I'll eat you right now!"

But the Gingerbread Boy said,
"You'll have to catch me first!
The old woman cannot catch me.
The horse cannot catch me.
And YOU cannot catch me, either!"
The bear ran as fast as he could.
But the Gingerbread Boy ran faster.
A crow was sitting up in a tree.
It saw the Gingerbread Boy.

"My, how good you smell!" it said.
"I think I'll eat you right now!"

But the Gingerbread Boy said,
"You'll have to catch me first!
The old woman cannot catch me.
The horse cannot catch me.
The bear cannot catch me.
And YOU cannot catch me, either."

The crow flew down and tried
to grab the Gingerbread Boy.

But he ran faster than ever,
and it could not catch him.

By and by, the Gingerbread Boy
came to some trees by a lake.
A fox was resting under a bush.
The fox saw him and called,
"Gingerbread Boy, you look tired!
Come rest a while with me."

But the Gingerbread Boy wouldn't.
"Oh, no, Mr. Fox," he said.

"I know you want to eat me, too.
But you'll have to catch me first!
The old woman cannot catch me.
The horse cannot catch me.
The bear cannot catch me.
The crow cannot catch me.
And YOU cannot catch me, either!"

At this, the sly old fox said,
"I can't hear you, Gingerbread Boy.
Please come a little closer."

The Gingerbread Boy went
a little closer to the fox.
He said in a loud voice, "I said,
The old woman cannot catch me.
The horse cannot catch me.
The bear cannot catch me.
The crow cannot catch me.
And YOU cannot catch me, either!"

The fox said, "I still can't hear!
Please come just a little closer."

So the Gingerbread Boy went
very close to the fox.
He said in a very loud voice,
"The old woman cannot catch me!
The horse cannot catch me!
The bear cannot catch me!
The crow cannot catch me!
And YOU cannot catch me, either!"

Then the fox cried,
"Ho, ho! Is that so?"

Quick as a wink the fox grabbed
the Gingerbread Boy and ate him
all up.

He didn't give a crumb
to the old woman or the horse
or the bear or the crow.

The Pot That Danced

Once upon a time a poor man
and his wife lived on a little farm.
The man's name was Hans.
His wife's name was Gerta.
They had five boys and five girls.

One day Gerta said to Hans,
"We have no food at all.
But the children must eat.
What shall we do?"

"I will sell the cow," said Hans.
"Then we will have money.
We can buy food with it."

So Hans said good-by and started
to take the cow to town.
Along the way he met a man carrying
a pot with three legs.

The man said, "What a fine cow!"

"Will you buy her?" asked Hans.
"I shall be happy to sell her."

The man said, "I have no money.
But I'll give this pot for your cow."

At first Hans would not.
Then all at once the pot began
to dance around on its three legs.
As it danced, it sang this song:
    "Oh, Hans, if you take me,
        Most happy will you be!"
    Then Hans thought, "What a pot!
It can dance and sing, too!
How the children will love it!"

So he gave the man his cow
and took the pot home with him.

When he got home, Gerta asked,
"How much money did you get
for the cow?"

"No money at all," said Hans.
"I sold the cow for this pot."

"What? For a pot?" cried Gerta.
"But we must have money!
We must have food!"

Just then the pot began to sing:
"Clean me! Clean me!
Then happy be!"
So Gerta cleaned the pot
till it was all bright and shining.
Then the pot began to dance.
It danced around the room.
It danced out of the house.
It danced down the road.
It danced into a rich man's house.

In this house the rich man's cook
was making a big pudding.
He saw the nice clean pot and said,
"I shall cook my pudding in that pot."
So he put all kinds of good things
into the pot to make the pudding.
He did not stop till the pot was full.
Then the pot began to dance again.
It danced out of the rich man's house.
"Come back!" cried the cook.

But the little pot danced away.
It danced down the road.
It danced home to Hans and Gerta.

Hans and Gerta and the children
had a very fine dinner that day.
They ate and ate till they could eat
no more.

The next day the pot danced till
it came to the rich man's barn.

Some people were working there.
"Let's see how much this pot holds,"
they said to each other.

So they filled the pot with wheat.
Again the pot began to dance.

"Come back!" cried the people.

But the little pot danced on.
It danced down the road.
It danced home to Hans and Gerta.

Hans and Gerta were very happy.
They said, "Now we can make bread
with this good wheat."

The next day the pot danced
into the rich man's counting house.
The rich man was counting his money
and putting it into bags.
Then he saw the pot.

"I can use that pot, too," he said.
So he filled the pot with money.

Again the pot danced away.
The rich man called, "Come back!"
But the pot would not.
It danced home to Hans and Gerta.
When it got there, it danced round
and round and round and round.
It went so fast the money flew out
and rolled all over the floor.

After that, Hans and Gerta and
the children were never poor again.
Every day the pot would dance.
Then the five boys and the five girls
would take hands, and dance with it.